Gg
Hh
Ii
Jj
Kk
Ll
Mm
Uu
Vv
Ww
Xx
Yy
Zz

*Dear Parent,*

*The* My First Steps to Reading® *series is based on a teaching activity that helps children learn to recognize letters and their sounds. The use of predictable language patterns and repetition of familiar words will also help your child build a basic sight vocabulary. Your child will enjoy watching the characters in the books place imaginative objects in "letter boxes." You and your child can even create and fill your own letter box, using stuffed animals, cut-out pictures, or other objects beginning with the same letter. The things you can do together are limited only by your imagination. Learning letters will be fun—the first important step on the road to reading.*

*The Editors*

 Published by Scholastic Inc., 90 Old Sherman Turnpike, Danbury, Connecticut 06810,
by arrangement with The Child's World, Inc.
Scholastic offers a varied selection of children's book racks and tote bags. For details about ordering, please write to:
Scholastic At Home, 90 Old Sherman Turnpike, Danbury, CT 06810, Attention: Premium Department

Originally published as *My "a" Sound Box* by The Child's World, Inc.


ISBN 0-7172-6500-5

Printed in the U.S.A.

# My "a" Book

(This book concentrates on the short "a" sound in the story line.
Words beginning with the long "a" sound are
included at the end of the book.)

*written by* Jane Belk Moncure
*illustrated by* Colin King

Little had a box.

"I will find things that begin with my 'a' sound," he said.

"I will put them into my sound box."

Little a put on his hat and went for a walk.

He found apples,
apples,
apples.

Did he put the apples into his box?

He did.

Little a found an alligator.

Did he put the ants into his box with the apples and the alligator?

He did.

Then Little a found toy arrows.

Guess where he put the arrows?

Next, Little a found an anchor.

Guess where he put the anchor?

Now the box was so full . . .

the ants,

the arrows,

and the anchor fell out.

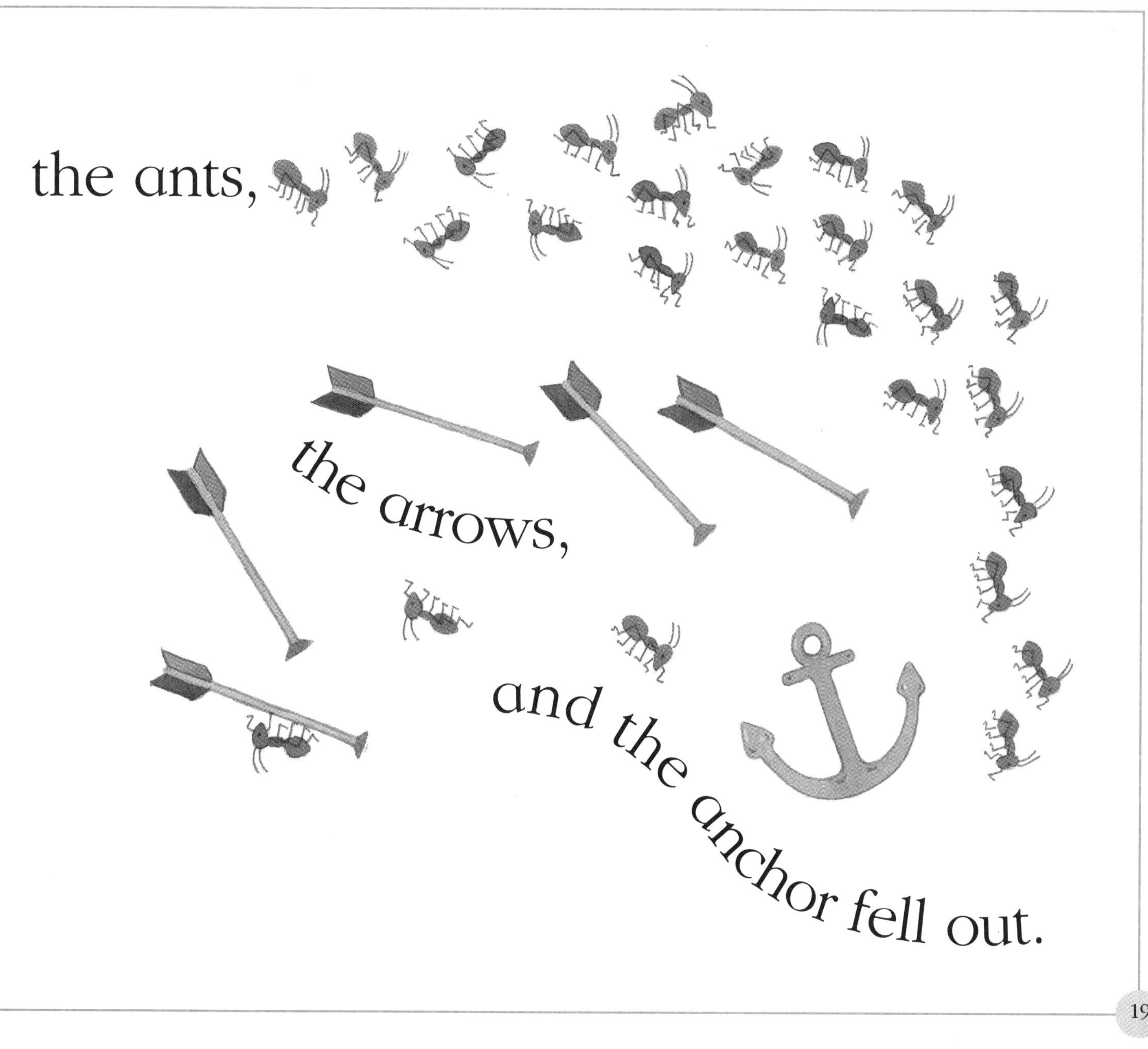

The apples

and the alligator

fell out, too.

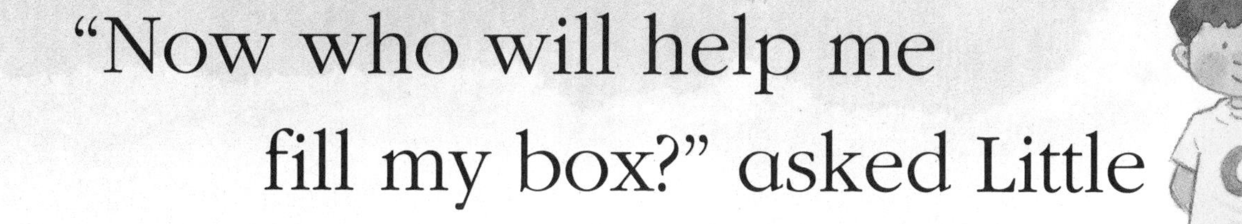

"Now who will help me
fill my box?" asked Little .

Just then, an astronaut came by.

“I will help you,”

said the astronaut.

"We will fill your box."
Guess what happened next?

The astronaut took

Little a for a ride.

# Up, up, and away they went!

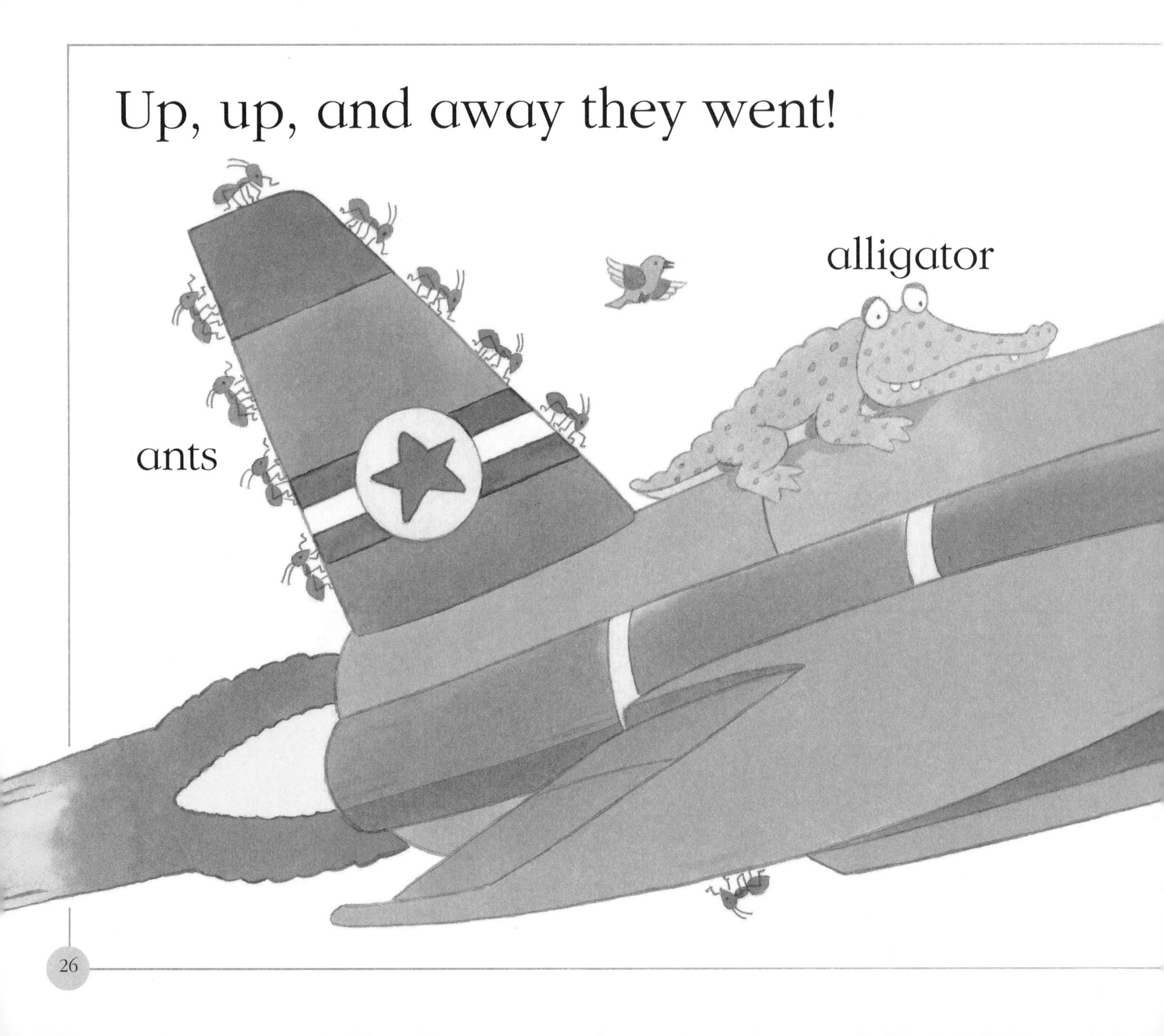

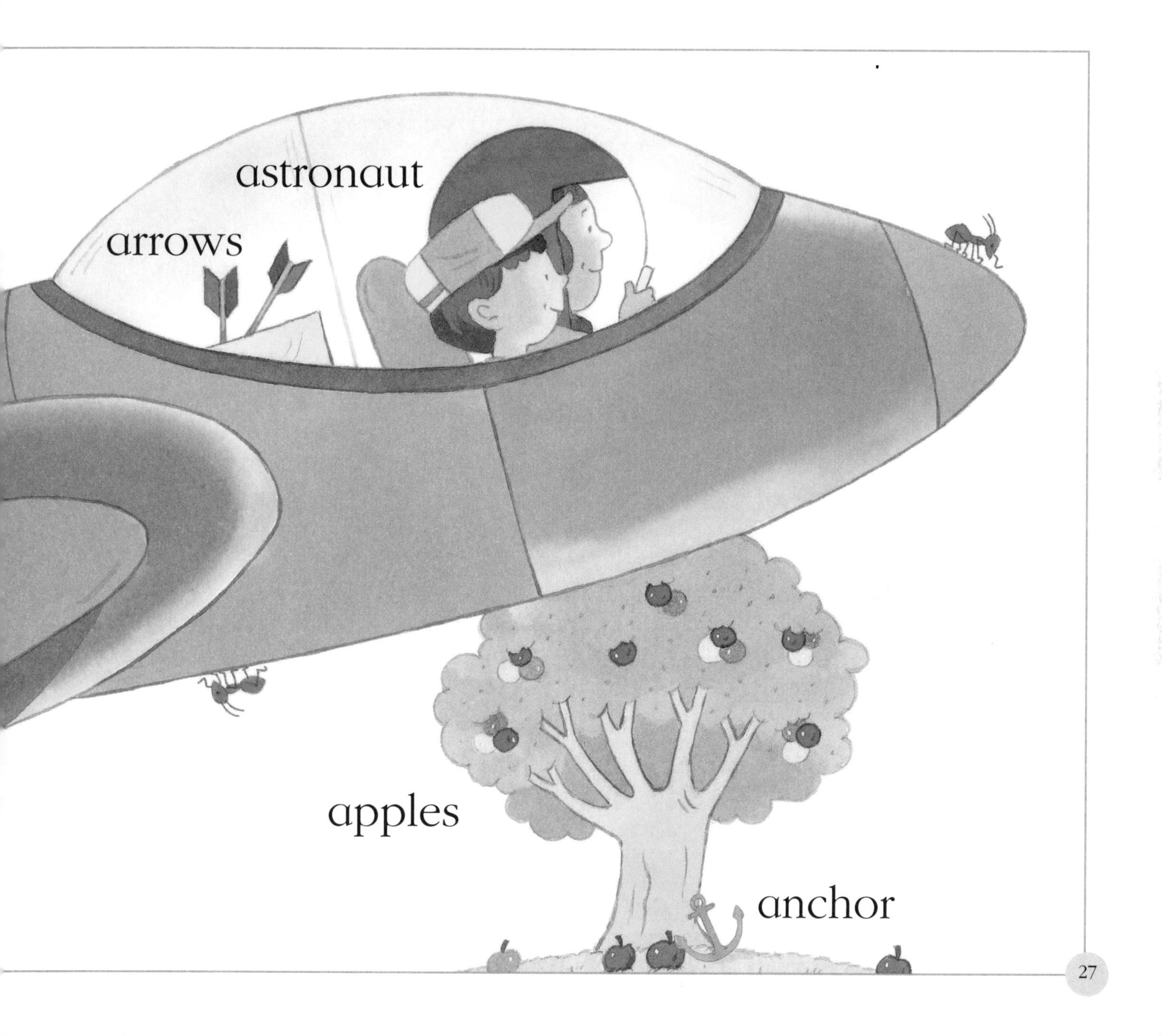
astronaut
arrows
apples
anchor

Can you read these words
with Little a?
antlers
acrobat
animals

Little a has another sound in some words. He says his name, "a."

Can you read these words?

Listen for Little a's name.

acorn

apron

ape

angel

Aa
Bb
Cc
Dd
Ee
Ff
Nn
Oo
Pp
Qq
Rr
Ss
Tt
My First Steps to READING®